At the Library

by Rachel Johns
illustrated by Caroline Keys

SCHOOL PUBLISHERS

Requests for permission to make copies of any part of the work should be addressed to School Permissions and Copyrights, Harcourt, Inc., 6277 Sea Harbor Drive, Orlando, Florida 32887–6777. Fax: 407-345-2418.

HARCOURT and the Harcourt Logo are trademarks of Harcourt, Inc., registered in the United States of America and/or other jurisdictions.

Printed in the United States of America

ISBN 10: 0-15-350444-7
ISBN 13: 978-0-15-350444-0

Ordering Options
ISBN 10: 0-15-350332-7 (Grade 2 Below-Level Collection)
ISBN 13: 978-0-15-350332-0 (Grade 2 Below-Level Collection)
ISBN 10: 0-15-357453-4 (package of 5)
ISBN 13: 978-0-15-357453-5 (package of 5)

1 2 3 4 5 6 7 8 9 10   179   15 14 13 12 11 10 09 08 07 06

Characters

Teacher

Librarian 1

Librarian 2

Drew

Claire

Setting: At the library

Teacher: Good morning, librarians. This is Drew. This is Claire. They are students from my class.

Librarians: Hello.

Drew: The children at our school would like to know about the library and your visiting author.

Claire: We'd like to ask you some questions. Then we'll report back to them.

5

Drew: Why do we have a library?

Librarian 1: Reading is important for everyone. We serve the people.

Claire: What do you mean by that?

Librarian 2: The library is here for anyone to use. Different people like to read different books. They all have different personalities.

Teacher: That's true!

Drew: Why did you ask an author to visit your library?

Librarian 1: We hope a visiting author will bring more people to the library to see what is here.

Claire: How did you decide who to invite?

Librarian 1: When we first talked about asking an author, we asked people to write down authors they would like to meet. Many ideas were delivered to the library.

Librarian 2: We want lots of people to attend. We thought about our choice of author very carefully.

Librarian 1: We were serious about making the right decision.

Librarian 2: We exchanged ideas, and we decided to invite Andrew Towers.

Teacher: Children love his books.

Librarian 1: We have to admit, getting such a popular author was extremely hard to accomplish.

Drew: How will you take care of the crowd?

Librarian 2: We will have an area with comfortable chairs.

Librarian 1: There will be food and drink.

Claire: Will Mr. Towers be staying for more than one day?

Librarian 2: No, it wasn't feasible. He's a very busy man.

Teacher: Thank you for answering our questions.

Drew: I have one more question. What will Andrew do at the library?

Librarian 1: He will read some of his stories out loud.

Librarian 2: He will give away some of his books, too.

Drew: I'll be here.

Claire: So will I.

Teacher: I will be here, too. Andrew's books are great!

Think Critically

1. What tells you that this story is a Readers' Theater?

2. Why was Andrew Towers important to the story?

3. How was the library going to take care of the crowd during Andrew Towers' visit?

4. Do you think many people would have gone to the library for Andrew Towers' visit?

5. If you could be a character in this story, who would you be? Why?

 **Social Studies**

Write a Paragraph Books can be bought from bookstores. Think about how a bookstore makes money. Write a paragraph with your ideas.

School-Home Connection Tell family members about the story. Then talk about authors you like and why you like their books.

Word Count: 351